Time to S
Poems for

Selected by
LEE BENNETT HOPKINS
and
MISHA ARENSTEIN

Illustrated by Lisl Weil

SCHOLASTIC BOOK SERVICES
NEW YORK • TORONTO • LONDON • AUCKLAND • SYDNEY • TOKYO

1st printing ....March 1973

Printed in the U.S.A.

For reprint permission grateful acknowledgment is made to:

ACKNOWLEDGMENTS

Every reasonable effort has been made to trace the owners of copyright materials in this book, but in some instances this has proven impossible. The publishers will be glad to receive information leading to more complete acknowledgments in subsequent printings of the book and, in the meantime, extend their apologies for any omissions.

Addison-Wesley Publishing Company for "Tombstone" from OODLES OF NOODLES, text © 1964 by Lucia M. and James L. Hymes, Jr., a Young Scott Book.

American Red Cross Youth News for "Spring" by Larry Cunningham, Paxton Wilt School, Louisville, Kentucky.

Atheneum Publishers, Inc., for 12 lines of "Time" and "When Dinosaurs Ruled the Earth" © 1963 by Patricia Hubbell from THE APPLE VENDOR'S FAIR; "Landscape" © 1970 by Eve Merriam; "Forsythia Bush" and "Snowy Morning" and "Winter Dark" from I THOUGHT I HEARD THE CITY, text copyright © 1969 by Lilian Moore; "August" and "On a Bike" from THE MALIBU AND OTHER POEMS, text copyright © 1972 by Myra Cohn Livingston.

The Bobbs-Merrill Company, Inc., for "Imagine Me on an Island" from CERTAINLY, CARRIE, CUT THE CAKE, copyright © 1971 by Margaret and John Travers Moore.

William Cole for "Sister Lettie's Ready" by Shel Silverstein, © 1967 by Shel Silverstein, from RHYME GIGGLES, edited by William Cole; and "Oh, Did You Hear?" by Shel Silverstein, © 1961 by Shel Silverstein from POEMS FOR SEASONS AND CELEBRATIONS, edited by William Cole. Both books were published by World Publishing Company.

Columbia University Press for "If Flowers Want to Grow" by David Ignatow, from POEMS 1934-1969.

The Cresset Press, Ltd., for "Boy Fishing" by E. J. Scovell.

Thomas Y. Crowell Company, Inc., for "First Thanksgiving" and selection from "In the Middle of the Night" and "New Year's Eve" from SKIP AROUND THE YEAR by Aileen Fisher. Copyright © 1967 by Aileen Fisher.

Curtis Brown, Ltd., for "The Museum Door" and "No Matter," copyright © 1973 by Lee Bennett Hopkins.

Contents

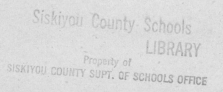

TIME...

IS ALL TIMES

from *Time*

I took today to bed with me
When I turned out the light,
And held it very closely
Through the cool, dark night.
I tucked it near my pillow
So that I could hear
All the things that filled it
With my nighttime ear.
I held it very close to me —
It could not get away —
And yet when morning came again
It was another day.

PATRICIA HUBBELL

How Many Seconds in a Minute?

How many seconds in a minute?
Sixty, and no more in it.

How many minutes in an hour?
Sixty for sun and shower.

How many hours in a day?
Twenty-four for work and play.

How many days in a week?
Seven both to hear and speak.

How many weeks in a month?
Four, as the swift moon runn'th.

How many months in a year?
Twelve the almanack makes clear.

How many years in an age?
One hundred says the sage.

How many ages in time?
No one knows the rhyme.

CHRISTINA G. ROSSETTI

There Isn't Time!

There isn't time, there isn't time
To do the things I want to do,
With all the mountain-tops to climb,
And all the woods to wander through,
And all the seas to sail upon,
And everywhere there is to go,
And all the people, every one
Who lives upon the earth, to know.
There's only time, there's only time
To know a few, and do a few,
And then sit down and make a rhyme
About the rest I want to do.

ELEANOR FARJEON

Hurry

Hurry, says the crossing guard,
the light's turning red.

Hurry, says the monitor,
straighten up the line.

Hurry, says the teacher,
hand in papers now.

Hurry, says the mother,
supper's getting cold.

Hurry, says the father,
time to go to bed.

Slowly, says the darkness,
you can talk to me.

EVE MERRIAM

Imagine me on an island —
All, all alone!
    I'd splash in the waves
    that lapped the shore,
    I'd count the shells
    on the ocean floor,
    I'd watch the clouds
    sweep idly by,
    and in imagination I
Would like it — all alone!
    None to tell me
    what to keep,
    none to say
    "Now go to sleep."
    Instead, my time
    would be my own
    And I would like it —
All alone!

MARGARET AND JOHN TRAVERS MOORE

The Errand

I rode my pony one summer day
Out to a farm far away
Where not one of the boys I knew
Had ever wandered before to play.

Up to a tank on top of a hill
That drips into a trough a spill
That when my pony drinks it dry
Its trickling takes all day to fill;

On to a windmill a little below
That brings up rusty water slow,
Squeaking and pumping only when
A lazy breeze decides to blow;

Then past a graveyard overgrown
With gourds and grass, where every stone
Leans crookedly against the sun,
Where I had never gone alone.

Down a valley I could see
Far away, one house and one tree
And a flat, green pasture out to the sky,
Just as I knew the farm would be!

I was taking a book my father sent
Back to the friendly farmer who lent
It to him, but who wasn't there;
I left it inside, and away I went!

Nothing happened. The sun set,
The moon came slowly up, and yet
When I was home at last, I knew
I'd been on an errand I'd never forget.

HARRY BEHN

Watching TV Cowboy Fights

Harum-scarum,
Rip 'em, tear 'em,
Shoot 'em up, boot 'em up,
Mash 'em, smash 'em.
Pounce 'em, trounce 'em,
Then denounce 'em.
Hit 'em, quit 'em,
Then outwit 'em.

Bang, bang, bang.
That's all, gang.
Gee!
I'm glad it's not me.

MARCI RIDLON

from
A Poem About the Glory of
The Football Pass

it's like see i'm
　　standing in the middle of the street . . .
and i throw this long pass with my football
　　and it's like a perfect spiral down the middle
　　of the street, it follows the white dotted
　　line, and my brother catches it
on the run, and it's like
　　　　in Yankee Stadium against the Packers,
and just now the street lights go on,
and a car turns the corner and heads for me.

STEVE LIGHT

On a bike

A curve came winding in the road
To make me stop.
I eased the brakes
To slow
    just where the city makes
    its pattern in the earth below.

The eucalyptus leaves blew clean.
I held my breath.
A dusty toad
Bulged gray
    and bulbous in the road.
    Then, next, a darting blue of jay

Streaked past the moment where I stood
In world so blue.
A pile of leaves
Lay dead
    until a crazy breeze
    stirred up the dusty road ahead

And there was someone in a car
Came roaring by.

He slammed his brakes
And cursed
   and asked the road to take.
   "This is the worst

Old mountain road!" he yelled.
The dust flew up.
He started down
The road.
   I watched him head to town
   and looked again to find the toad

And jay. But they had gone.
The place was dry,
All out of tune
And brown.
   "Why waste the whole good afternoon
   Up here?" I asked myself, and hurried down.

MYRA COHN LIVINGSTON

Watching Things

Now I'm stretched out on my stomach,
Watching things walking in the grass.
Most of the things I see are small —
Like ants. There's an anthill nearby.
And I like best to put crumbs down
And watch the ants take them back home.
Sometimes I stop them with a stick,
But mostly I just watch them go.
It must be very hard, I think,
To carry a crumb
When you're hardly as big as one.

MARCI RIDLON

The Boy Fishing

I am cold and alone,
On my tree-root sitting as still as stone.
The fish come to my net. I scorned the sun,
The voices on the road, and they have gone.
My eyes are buried in the cold pond, under
The cold, spread leaves; my thoughts
      are silver-wet.
I have ten stickleback, a half-day's plunder,
Safe in my jar. I shall have ten more yet.

E. J. SCOVELL

Homework

Homework sits on top of Sunday, squashing
    Sunday flat.
Homework has the smell of Monday, homework's
    very fat
Heavy books and piles of paper, answers
    I don't know.
Sunday evening's almost finished, now
    I'm going to go
Do my homework in the kitchen. Maybe
    just a snack,
Then I'll sit right down and start as soon
    as I run back
For some chocolate sandwich cookies.
    Then I'll really do
All that homework in a minute. First I'll
    see what new
Show they've got on television in the living room.
Everybody's laughing there, but misery and gloom
And a full refrigerator are where I am at.
I'll just have another sandwich. Homework's
    very fat.

RUSSELL HOBAN

The Museum Door

What's behind the museum door?

Ancient necklaces,
African art,
The armor of knights,
A peasant cart;

Priceless old coins,
A king's golden throne,
Mummies in linen,
And a dinosaur bone.

LEE BENNETT HOPKINS

Hide and Seek

Call out. Call loud: "I'm ready! Come and
    find me!"
The sacks in the toolshed smell like the seaside.
They'll never find you in this salty dark,
But be careful that your feet aren't sticking out.
Wiser not to risk another shout.
The floor is cold. They'll probably be searching
The bushes near the swing. Whatever happens
You musn't sneeze when they come prowling in.
And here they are, whispering at the door;
You've never heard them sound so hushed before.
Don't breathe. Don't move. Stay dumb. Hide in
    your blindness.
They're moving closer, someone stumbles, mutters;
Their words and laughter scuffle, and they're gone.

But don't come out just yet; they'll try the lane
And then the greenhouse and back here again.
They must be thinking that you're very clever,
Getting more puzzled as they search all over.
It seems a long time since they went away.
Your legs are stiff, the cold bites through your coat;
The dark damp smell of sand moves in your throat.
It's time to let them know that you're the winner.
Push off the sacks. Uncurl and stretch.
        That's better!
Out of the shed and call to them: "I've won!
Here I am! Come and own up I've caught you!"
The darkening garden watches. Nothing stirs.
The bushes hold their breath; the sun is gone.
Yes, here you are. But where are they who
        sought you?

Snowy Morning

Wake
gently this morning
to a different day.
Listen.
There is no bray
of buses,
no brake growls,
no siren howls and
no horns
blow.
There is only
the silence
of a city
hushed
by snow.

LILIAN MOORE

Skiing

Fast as foxes,
buzzy as bees,
down the slope
on our silver-tipped skis —

early in the morning
Roseanna and I
far from our house
on the hilltop fly.

A snowbird's yawning,
the sky's all pink,
somewhere in the valley
the lights still blink.

No one's awake
but us, and a bird.
The day's too beautiful
to speak a word.

ROSE BURGUNDER

TIME...

IS A YEAR

That cheerful snowman
Guarding our door
Never will
See our daffodils.

HANNAH LYONS JOHNSON

from Ground Hog's Holiday

The second month, the second day,
We know is Ground Hog's Holiday.
The keeper of the local zoo,
Photographers, reporters, too,
Anxiously await together
Woodchuck's forecast of the weather.

MIRIAM GOLDSTEIN

March

A blue day,
a blue jay
and a good beginning.
One crow,
melting snow —
spring's winning!

ELIZABETH COATSWORTH

Spring

There's a nice smell to Spring —
   It's fresh, clean, and cool.
Sometimes after a rain,
   As I walk home from school,
I want to open our door wide
   And bring the whole outdoors inside.

LARRY CUNNINGHAM

Forsythia Bush

There is nothing
quite
like the sudden
light

of
forsythia
that
one morning
without warning

explodes
into yellow
and
startles the street
into spring.

LILIAN MOORE

The spring
day
closes,

Lingering

where
there
is
water.

ISSA

Summer Snow

An evening by the sea
just before the night
the fishing pier turned
a feathery white,
a lovely white, just as though
all those gulls
were summer snow.

CHARLOTTE ZOLOTOW

No Matter

No matter
how hot-burning
it is
outside.

when

you peel a
long, fat cucumber

or

cut deep into
a fresh, ripe watermelon

you can
feel
coolness
come into your hands.

LEE BENNETT HOPKINS

August

Mike says
we ought to have
a swimming party.

Fine, I answer,
but where will we
have this party?

Here, he says,
pointing to the fire hydrant.
Here, he says,
when we turn it on.

We'll have a party
and invite
Alex and
any guy who wants to swim

Stand-
ing
up.

MYRA COHN LIVINGSTON

August

The city dwellers all complain
When August comes and brings no rain.
The pavements burn upon their feet;
Temper and temperature compete.
They mop their brows, they slow their pace,
And wish they were some other place.

But farmers do not mind the heat;
They know it ripens corn and wheat.
They love to see the sun rise red,
Remembering what their fathers said:
"An August month that's dry and warm
Will never do the harvest harm."

MICHAEL LEWIS

Sunning

Old Dog lay in the summer sun
Much too lazy to rise and run.
He flapped an ear
At a buzzing fly.
He winked a half opened
Sleepy eye.
He scratched himself
On an itching spot,
As he dozed on the porch
Where the sun was hot.
He whimpered a bit
From force of habit
While he lazily dreamed
Of chasing a rabbit.
But Old Dog happily lay in the sun
Much too lazy to rise and run.

JAMES S. TIPPETT

Indoors

The doors are closing;
summer's gone:
harbor and hazard,
sand and sail,
hammock and haystack,
barn and briar
fences and fairgrounds,
treetop, trail.

Now in my alphabet
of hours
are notebooks, numbers,
nary a lawn.
A clock ticks slowly
in the room.
Time is beginning;
summer's gone.

ROSE BURGUNDER

from *In the Middle of the Night*

In the fall
when noisy crickets
went iddle-diddle
in the middle
of fields and thickets
before nights turned chill
and the grass got brittle,
I wondered how anything so *little*
could be so shrill.
I wished I could find one,
and slip up behind one,
and see how he did it.
I wished I could see
if he really had a fiddle
and solve the riddle
of where he hid it.

AILEEN FISHER

What Night Would It Be?

If the moon shines
On the black pines
And an owl flies
And a ghost cries
And the hairs rise
On the back
  on the back
    on the back of your neck —

If you look quick
At the moon-slick
On the black air
And what goes there
Rides a broom-stick
And if things pick
At the back
  at the back
    at the back of your neck —

Would you know then
By the small men
With the lit grins
And with no chins,

By the owl's *hoo*,
And the ghost's *boo*,
By the Tom Cat,
And the Black Bat
On the night air,
And the thing there,
By the thing,
   by the thing,
      by the dark thing there

(Yes, you do,
yes, you do
know the thing I mean)

That it's now,
   that it's now,
      that it's — Halloween!

JOHN CIARDI

November Night

Listen . . .
With faint dry sound,
Like steps of passing ghosts
The leaves, frost-crisp'd, break from the trees
And fall.

ADELAIDE CRAPSEY

First Thanksgiving

Venison for stew and roasting,
oysters in the ashes toasting,
geese done to a turn,
berries (dried) and wild grapes (seeded)
mixed with dough and gently kneaded —
what a feast to earn!

Indian corn in strange disguises,
ash cakes, hoe cakes (many sizes),
kernels roasted brown . . .
after months of frugal living
what a welcome first Thanksgiving
there in Plymouth town!

AILEEN FISHER

Winter Dark

Winter dark comes early
mixing afternoon
and night.
Soon
there's a comma of a moon,

and each street light
along the
way
puts its period
to the end of day.

Now
a neon sign
punctuates the dark
with a bright
blinking
breathless
exclamation mark!

LILIAN MOORE

Winter Is Tacked Down

Hurrah!

Hurray!

It snowed last night.

Today
   the green lawn
   is whiskered with white.

Look around —
   enough snow on the ground
   for a snowball.

Scoop it up in your hands,
   gloves or no.
Wad it,
   pack it tight,
      round,
       big.

Let go!

Smash!
Splash!

Winter is here!

You can't hold winter back,
   not possibly,
      once you have tacked a snowball
      to the trunk of a tree.

SISTER NOEMI WEYGANT

I Heard a Bird Sing

I heard a bird sing
In the dark of December
A magical thing
And sweet to remember:

"We are nearer to Spring
Than we were in September,"
I heard a bird sing
In the dark of December.

OLIVER HERFORD

Christmas Eve

On a winter night
When the moon is low
The rabbits hop on the frozen snow.
The woodpecker sleeps in his hole in the tree.
And fast asleep is the chickadee.

Twelve o'clock
And the world is still
As the Christmas star comes over the hill.
The angels sing, and sing again
"Peace on earth, goodwill to men."

MARION EDEY

New Year's Eve

Hear the horns and rattles,
hear the trumpets blow,
sending out a message
through the cold and snow:
"Thank you for your favors,
Old Year, as you go."

Hear the bells and cheering,
hear the whistles cry,
sending out a message
through the winter sky:
"Glad to see you, New Year,
Keep our spirits high."

AILEEN FISHER

I Resolve

Resolutions I don't make
  I can't break.
SO I RESOLVE not to make any —
  Then I can't break any.

MARGARET FISHBACK

TIME...

FOR OUR EARTH

Hurt no living thing:
Ladybird nor butterfly,
Nor moth with dusty wing,
Nor cricket chirping cheerily,
Nor grasshopper so light of leap,
Nor dancing gnat, nor beetle fat,
Nor harmless worms that creep.

CHRISTINA ROSSETTI

When Dinosaurs Ruled The Earth

Brontosaurus, diplodocus, gentle trachodon,
Dabbled in the muds of time,
Once upon, upon.

Tyrannosaurus raised his head
And rolled his evil eye,
Bared his long and yellow teeth
And bid his neighbors 'bye.
His pygmy brain was slow to grasp
The happenings of the day,
And so he roamed and slew his friends
And ate without delay.

Brontosaurus, diplodocus, gentle trachodon,
Dabbled in the muds of time,
Once upon, upon.

Allosaurus awed his foe,
He awed his friends who passed,
His teeth were made for tearing flesh,
His teeth were made to gnash.
Taller than a building now,
Taller than a tree,
He roamed about the swamp-filled world
And ate his company.

Brontosaurus, diplodocus, gentle trachodon,
Dabbled in the muds of time,
Once upon, upon.

    Eaters of their friends and foe
    Or dabblers in the slime,
    Their pygmy brains were slow to grasp,
    Once upon a time.

PATRICIA HUBBELL

Swift Things Are Beautiful

Swift things are beautiful:
Swallows and deer,
And lightning that falls
Bright-veined and clear,
Rivers and meteors,
Wind in the wheat,
The strong-withered horse,
The runner's sure feet.

And slow things are beautiful:
The closing of day,
The pause of the wave
That curves downward to spray,
The ember that crumbles,
The opening flower,
And the ox that moves on
In the quiet of power.

ELIZABETH COATSWORTH

The Good Earth

The earth is what gives us life,
food, and also shelter.
The earth, when it's tired,
refuses to give life.
Woe to the people when it doesn't give life!

KATHY ITTA

The Apple Tree

Near that rusty
railway track,
an ugly, junky scene,
blooms a little
flowering tree
radiant as a queen.

CHARLOTTE ZOLOTOW

56

Unfair

It doesn't seem fair
that a tree
that makes such
a good place
to hang your swing
and gives shade
to people on hot days
and homes
to birds and chipmunks
could someday
get to be
a paper napkin.

BOBBI KATZ

Discovery

In a puddle left from last week's rain,
   A friend of mine whose name is Joe
Caught a tadpole, and showed me where
   Its froggy legs were beginning to grow.

Then we turned over a musty log,
   With lichens on it in a row,
And found some fiddleheads of ferns
   Uncoiling out of the moss below.

We hunted around, and saw the first
   Jack-in-the-pulpits beginning to show,
   And even discovered under a rock
   Where spotted salamanders go.

   I learned all this one morning from Joe,
   But how much more there is to know!

HARRY BEHN

   As asphalt and concrete
   Replace bushes and trees,
   As highways and buildings
   Replaces marshes and woods,
   What will replace
   The song of the birds?

TONY CHEN

Where?

Mrs. Chipmunk,
  alone,
  on a stone,
     why are you so fat?

I know,
I know,
  you're like my cat —
     you're going to have babies.

I wish,
  I wish
  that I knew where,
  for I would hold one —
     oh, so carefully.

SISTER NOEMI WEYGANT

To a Squirrel
at Kyle-na-no

Come play with me;
Why should you run
Through the shaking tree
As though I'd a gun
To strike you dead?
When all I would do
Is to scratch your head
And let you go.

W. B. YEATS

To Look
at
Any Thing

To look at any thing,
If you would know that thing,
You must look at it long:
To look at this green and say
"I have seen spring in these
Woods," will not do — you must
Be the thing you see:
You must be the dark snakes of
Stems and ferny plumes of leaves,
You must enter in
To the small silences between
The leaves,
You must take your time
And touch the very peace
They issue from.

JOHN MOFFITT

Landscape

What will you find at the edge of the world?
A footprint,
a feather,
desert sand swirled?
A tree of ice,
a rain of stars,
or a junkyard of cars?

What will there be at the rim of the earth?
A mollusc,
a mammal,
a new creature's birth?
Eternal sunrise,
immortal sleep,
or cars piled up in a rusty heap?

EVE MERRIAM

TIME...

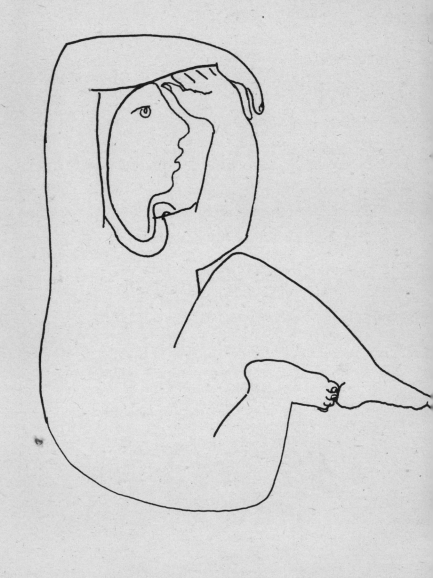

FOR SHORT THOUGHTS

A Word

A word is dead
When it is said,
  Some say.

I say it just
Begins to live
  That day.

EMILY DICKINSON

I catch a firefly
        In cupped hands. My fingers glow
With imprisoned fire.

REBECCA CAUDILL

They utter no sound —
        The midge, the beetle, the ant —
Yet I hear them sing.

REBECCA CAUDILL

Even among insects in this world,
        Some are good at singing,
        Some bad.

ISSA

How sadly the bird in his cage
Watches the butterflies.

ISSA

Birds are flying past me
and a lonely feeling
has come over me.

DEBRA FONG

If Flowers Want to Grow

If flowers want to grow
right out of concrete sidewalk cracks
I'm going to bend down to smell them

DAVID IGNATOW

Galloping pony —
alone, against the moonlight,
on a whitened beach.

KYORAI

Little frog among
rain-shaken leaves, are you, too,
splashed with fresh green paint?

GAKI

Bubbles

Two bubbles found they had rainbows on
    their curves.
They flashed out saying:
"It was worth being a bubble just to have held
    that rainbow thirty seconds."

CARL SANDBURG

Rocks

Big rocks into pebbles,
pebbles into sand.
I really hold a million million rocks here
    in my hand.

FLORENCE PARRY HEIDE

These are
Two happy times —
Watching a baseball game,
Seeing your baby brother walking
Alone.

JOHN VITALE

Poem

I loved my friend.
He went away from me.
There's nothing more to say.
The poem ends,
Soft as it began —
I loved my friend.

LANGSTON HUGHES

sometimes i have friends
and then
there is only me.

MELANIE RAY

TIME...

TO LAUGH

Sister Lettie's Ready

A wonderful thing happened to my
   sister Lettie, it did;
Instead of hair, she grew a lot of
   spaghetti, she did.
And now whenever she wants a
   snack at night, she does,
She simply combs it down and
   takes a bite, she does.

SHEL SILVERSTEIN

I Know an Owl

I know an owl
   Who uses a towel
To dry himself after it rains.
"I hate being wet," he explains.

EDWARD ANTHONY

The Housing Shortage

A country mouse
Lives in a house,
But city mice
Are short of hice.

MARGARET FISHBACK

Sour Puss

I have a greedy, part-time cat
Who answers to the name of "Scat."

Imperious and bland as Nero,
He thinks he's everybody's hero.

He haughtily accepts my liver,
Nor does he ever thank the giver.

When he is through, he goes next door
And arrogantly dines once more.

He never begs. He just demands,
And obviously understands

That when he's polished off our food,
It's we who swell with gratitude.

MARGARET FISHBACK

Identity Parade

No he wasn't very *tall*
      And, no, he wasn't very *short*
He was what you'd really call
      A fairly *ordinary* sort.

No, his hair it wasn't *dark*
      But then you'd hardly call it *fair;*
Not a color you'd remark,
      Just like — well, you know, like *hair!*

Yes his suit was sort of *brown*
      Though you could have called it *gray.*
Were his cuffs turned up or down?
      Now that I'd hardly like to say.

He was not exactly *fat*
      But then I wouldn't call him *thin.*
I don't *think* his feet were flat.
      His toes turned *out.* Or was it *in!*

His tie was vivid green,
      Or, half a minute, was it blue?
Well you know just what I mean:
      It was quite a brilliant hue.

His face was somewhat red,
      Or let me think now, was it pale?
He had a heavy lightsome tread.
      Oh, yes, I'm sure that he was male!

Would I know the man again?
      Do you take me for a dunce?
Out of twenty thousand men
      I'd recognize *that* man at once.

ANONYMOUS

Eat-it-all Elaine

I went away last August
To summer camp in Maine,
And there I met a camper
Called Eat-it-all Elaine.

Although Elaine was quiet,
She liked to cause a stir
By acting out the nickname
Her camp-mates gave to her.

The day of our arrival
At Cabin Number Three
When girls kept coming over
To greet Elaine and me,
She took a piece of Kleenex
And calmly chewed it up,
Then strolled outside the cabin
And ate a buttercup.

Elaine, from that day forward,
Was always in command.
On hikes, she'd eat some birch-bark
On swims, she'd eat some sand.
At meals, she'd swallow prune-pits
And never have a pain,
While everyone around her
Would giggle, "Oh, Elaine!"

One morning, berry-picking,
A bug was in her pail,
And though we thought for certain
Her appetite would fail,
Elaine said, "Hmm, a stinkbug."
And while we murmured, "Ooh,"
She ate her pail of berries
And ate the stinkbug, too.

The night of Final Banquet
When counselors were handing
Awards to different children
Whom they believed outstanding,
To every *thinking* person
At summer camp in Maine
The Most Outstanding Camper
Was Eat-it-all Elaine.

KAYE STARBIRD

from *Company*

I'm fixing a lunch for a dinosaur.
Who knows when one might come by?
I'm pulling up all the weeds I can find.
I'm piling them high as the sky.
I'm fixing a lunch for a dinosaur.
I hope he will stop by soon.
Maybe he'll just walk down my street
And stop for lunch at noon.

BOBBI KATZ

Sir Smasham Uppe

Good afternoon, Sir Smasham Uppe!
We're having tea: do take a cup.
Sugar and milk? Now let me see —
Two lumps, I think? . . . Good gracious me!
The silly thing slipped off your knee!
Pray don't apologize, old chap:
A very trivial mishap!
So clumsy of you? How absurd!
My dear Sir Smasham, not a word!
Now do sit down and have another,
And tell us about your brother —
You know, the one who broke his head.
Is the poor fellow still in bed?
A chair — allow me, sir! . . . Great Scott!
That *was* a nasty smash! Eh, what?
Oh, not at all: the chair was old —
Queen Anne, or so we have been told.
We've got at least a dozen more:
Just leave the pieces on the floor.
I want you to admire our view:
Come nearer to the window, do;
And look how beautiful . . . Tut, tut!
You didn't see that it was shut?

I hope you are not badly cut!
Not hurt? A fortunate escape!
Amazing! Not a single scrape!
And now, if you have finished tea,
I fancy you might like to see
A little thing or two I've got.
That china plate? Yes, worth a lot:
A beauty too . . . Ah, there it goes!
I trust it didn't hurt your toes?
Your elbow brushed it off the shelf?
Of course: I've done the same myself.
And now, my dear Sir Smasham — Oh,
You surely don't intend to go?
You *must* be off? Well, come again.
So glad you're fond of porcelain!

E. V. RIEU

Oh Did You Hear?

Oh did you hear?
The President has measles,
The Principal has just burned down the school,
Your hair is filled with jam and purple weasels.

April Fool!

SHELLEY SILVERSTEIN

The Cares of a Caretaker

A nice old lady by the sea
    Was neat as she was plain.
And every time the tide came in
    She swept it back again.

And when the sea untidy grew
    And waves began to beat,
She took her little garden rake
    And raked it smooth and neat.

She ran a carpet-sweeper up
    And down the pebbly sand,
She said. "This is the only way
    To keep it clean — good land!"

And when the gulls came strolling by,
    She drove them shrilly back,
Remarking that it spoiled the beach,
    "The way them birds do track."

She fed the catfish clotted cream
    And taught it how to purr —
And were a catfish so endowed
    She would have stroked its fur.

She stopped the little sea urchins
    That traveled by in pairs,
And washed their dirty faces clean
    And combed their little hairs.

She spread white napkins on the surf
    With which she fumed and fussed.
"When it ain't covered up," she said,
    "It gits all over dust."

She didn't like to see the ships
    With all the waves act free,
And so she got a painted sign
    Which read, "Keep off the Sea."

But dust and splutter as she might,
    Her work was sadly vain;
However oft she swept the beach,
    The tides came in again

And she was sometimes wan and worn
    When she retired to bed —
"A woman's work ain't never done,"
    That nice old lady said.

WALLACE IRWIN

Chocolate

Why did I forget the chocolate
I was saving in my pocket
When my blue jeans went into the washer?

RUSSELL HOBAN

Manual System

Mary has a thingamajig clamped on her ears
    And sits all day taking plugs out and sticking
        plugs in.
Flashes and flashes — voices and voices calling for
        ears to pour words in;
Faces at the end of wires asking for other
        faces at the end of other wires;
All day taking plugs out and sticking plugs in,
Mary has a thingamajig on her ears.

CARL SANDBURG

Tombstone

Here lies
A bully
Who wasn't so wise.
He picked on
A fellow
Who was his own size.

LUCIA M. HYMES
JAMES L. HYMES, JR.

Index of Titles and Authors'

Index of First Lines